FOREWORD

"The Giants of the Bay" is the journey of the Chesapeake Mermaid as she experiences big changes in her world. There is a growing concern for the environment and our future, but explaining the challenges involved can be overwhelming to children of any age. This storybook introduces those ideas through gentle characters with a colorful perspective on our Chesapeake Bay ecosystem. It also reminds us of our importance, no matter how small, and the value in trying, even if we fail on the way to our goal.

The story is inspiring, but it calls us to go one step further by exploring the world around us and having positive impact. We're all on this rock together. Let's make our waterways swimmable, fishable, and livable for everyone and for many years to come.

— *Jon Boesche', Host of "It's A Water Life," CBS Radio*

Magical Map of the Past

North
West · East
South

Big Indian Rock

Leight Park

Susquehanna

Gunpowder R.

Black's Marsh

Patapsco R.

Sassafras R.

Eastern Neck

Dyke Marsh

Jug Bay

Mallows Bay

Potomac R.

Patuxent R.

Chesapeake Bay

Zekiah Swamp

Battle Creek

Blackwater

Nanticoke R.

Rappahannock R.

Fishing Bay

Janes Island

Rappahannock River Valley

Pocomoke R.

James R.

York River Park

Pamunkey R.

York R.

The Wetlands

Brownsville Preserve

Atlantic Ocean

Paradise Creek

First Landing

Great Dismal Swamp

Map drawn with the help of John Smith, 1612

2

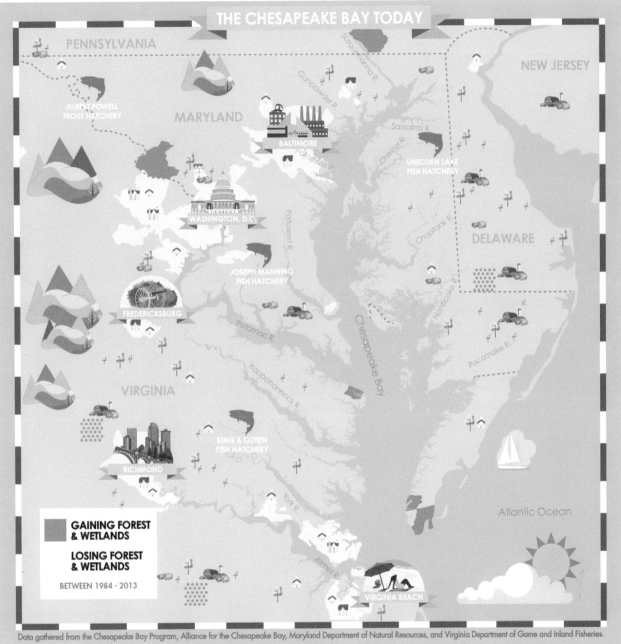

THE CHESAPEAKE BAY TODAY

PENNSYLVANIA

MARYLAND

NEW JERSEY

ALBERT POWELL
TROUT HATCHERY

BALTIMORE

Susquehanna R.

Gunpowder R.

Sassafras R.

Chester R.

UNICORN LAKE
FISH HATCHERY

Patapsco R.

WASHINGTON, D.C.

Patuxent R.

Choptank R.

DELAWARE

JOSEPH MANNING
FISH HATCHERY

Nanticoke R.

FREDERICKSBURG

Potomac R.

Chesapeake Bay

Pocomoke R.

Rappahannock R.

VIRGINIA

KING & QUEEN
FISH HATCHERY

RICHMOND

York R.

Atlantic Ocean

**GAINING FOREST
& WETLANDS**

**LOSING FOREST
& WETLANDS**

BETWEEN 1984 - 2013

James R.

VIRGINIA BEACH

Data gathered from the Chesapeake Bay Program, Alliance for the Chesapeake Bay, Maryland Department of Natural Resources, and Virginia Department of Game and Inland Fisheries.

Special thanks to my friends for their support and volunteer contributions,
my family for their endless love and encouragement,
and my sweetheart for being the best companion a mermaid could wish for.

ISBN-10: 0-9990602-2-8
ISBN-13: 978-0-9990602-2-3

The Chesapeake Mermaid &
The Giants of the Bay

Story by The Chesapeake Mermaid

Illustrated by Angela Rose Mitchell

Once upon a tide, the Chesapeake mermaid was exploring the waters of her home in the Chesapeake region, looking for her next adventure. Would she find an animal in need of rescue or maybe a person who could use a helping hand? She loved to do whatever she could to make the world a better place.

One day, she came across a great big footprint. Then another. Then another! Someone or something was making a huge impact on the environment. What could it be?

She followed the great big footprints through the dark sand, across the widgeon grass beds, towards the coastal marshes. "Ouch!" the mermaid exclaimed, as she suddenly hit her head on a big rock. All around her were rocks - lots and lots of huge rocks! Instead of her coastal marsh, she found herself at a hard shoreline as far as her eyes could see. And there, in the middle of it all, was a giant.

With rocks and wood and sand, the giant was changing the shoreline into something different.

Without the coastal marsh, where would the blue crabs start their families? Without underwater grasses, where would the seahorses hide? We needed eelgrass for much more than eels. So many fish, turtles, and birds had homes there, the mermaid couldn't begin to imagine the impact the giant had made in such a short time.

"BOOM! BOOM! BOOM! BOOM!" went the giant's footsteps.

The giant was running back and forth - moving handfuls of rocks, pulling armloads of plants, and scattering the animals and people who lived there. Sometimes the giant moved them again and again.

The mermaid wanted to help. "Excuse me!" she yelled from down below. "Hello up there! I have an idea I'd like to share." But the giant was far too big and busy to hear her very small voice. Before the mermaid could share her idea, the giant moved on, leaving huge changes behind.

The mermaid swam as fast as she could to catch up to the giant, but soon found herself tired and stopped to rest.

"Whoa!" the mermaid yelled as she got caught up in a school of shimmering menhaden. They flashed and sparkled in the sunlight as they made sharp turns together. She was quickly tossed and twirled and finally felt herself scooped up, up, up out of the water with all the fish. It was another giant - a hungry giant! Sitting in the giant's great big hand, she could not only see the menhaden, but also turtles, dolphins, and even seabirds as well. The giant wanted to eat the menhaden, but all the other animals got caught up in the meal too.

Unsatisfied, the giant dropped everything back into the water. The mermaid, fish, turtles, dolphins, seabirds, and everything else went tumbling into the bay.

"BOOM! BOOM! BOOM! BOOM!" went the giant's footsteps.

The giant scooped up water here and there - looking for the perfect meal - sometimes picking up the same things again and again. Nothing suited the giant's appetite.

The mermaid wanted to help. "Excuse me!" she yelled from down below. "Hello up there! I have an idea I'd like to share." But the giant was far too big and too busy to hear her very small voice. Before the mermaid could share her idea, the giant moved on, leaving huge changes behind.

Frustrated over not being heard, the mermaid decided to swim to a bayside town and talk to the townsfolk about the huge changes happening in the bay. When she arrived, there on the docks was a third giant.

Unlike the first two giants, this one appeared to be doing nothing at all. This giant smiled a giant smile and was adored by the people, who also appeared to be doing nothing but smiling.

"Can you make the huge changes we want?" yelled the townsfolk to the giant's left. "I sure can!" said the giant, leaning their way with a big smile. The people on the left cheered and marched away. "Can you make the huge changes we want?" yelled the townsfolk to his right. "I sure can!" said the giant, leaning their way with a big smile. The people on the right cheered and marched away.

They believed the giant would take care of everything for them, so they did nothing themselves.

19

The mermaid had waited a long time to speak to someone who could make huge changes. She approached the giant and once again said, "Excuse me! Hello up there!" The giant smiled and leaned in her way. "When will you be making these huge changes the townsfolk have asked for?" The giant looked at a giant watch and said, "Oh, in about... fifty years."

The mermaid realized great big things also had a great big calendar.

The mermaid went away feeling very small. Fifty years felt like a long time. When the huge changes were made, would they be responsible changes? Would those who made the changes help if there were problems?

She looked at the wildlife all around her and thought about the changes they made and how their lives fit together. Change can seem scary, but it looks like changes here happen in a good way. Maybe there was more she could do.

Sometimes problems can feel very big and we're not sure what to do, but we can always try.

The mermaid realized these were great big thoughts and she wanted to try to make changes even though she was very small. She had another idea and knew who would listen.

The mermaid came ashore near a group of children cleaning a beach. "Excuse me! Hello up there!" the mermaid called. "Will you help me plant some very important seeds?"

Can you guess what kind of seeds they were?

They were seeds of knowledge.

The mermaid told the children, "I believe in you. You will learn and grow and know how important it is to listen. And one day you will be giants making huge changes yourselves."

"When will that happen?" one child asked.

The mermaid hugged them close and whispered, "It will happen faster than you can imagine."

Science

Habitats

- The homes where animals or plants live
- The Chesapeake watershed includes forests, wetlands, rivers, marshes, reefs, shallow water, deep water, and more

Rip Rap

- Large rocks layered along shorelines to try to prevent erosion
- Can sometimes be replaced with "living shorelines"

Bycatch

- Animals accidentally caught while fishing for another animal
- Marine turtles and dolphins are examples, but any animal can be bycatch
- Modifying fishing gear and changing methods can reduce bycatch

Science

Development

- Changing nature to meet the goals of people, as in cutting down trees, building a house, or changing the path of a stream
- Our impact on nature can take a long time to see
- Some developed areas are being returned to their natural beauty and function

Industry

- People's use of nature, as in fishing, farming, or recreation
- Old methods relied on experience and guessing to make changes
- New technology is used to show improvements, give better options, and get better results

Policy

- Rules which help people meet common goals over time, as in limits, bans, or rewards
- In the past, few rules were enforced or made from limited viewpoints
- Different types of people are being included today than ever before

Be A Giant Today

- Start a nature journal or sketchbook
- Count how many things you throw away in a day, week, or month
- Swim and fish in areas with proper permission
- Learn about the wildlife in your yard
- Start a compost pile
- Talk about your future and what you would like to see and do
- Practice cleaning up and turning off lights when you leave a room
- Take pictures but leave feathers, shells, or flowers where you find them
- Create a garden with native plants
- Resist the urge to squash a bug and use a cup to move them instead
- Build a pollinator hotel to help local bees
- Drink from a reusable water bottle and carry it everywhere
- **Follow the Chesapeake Mermaid on social media**

ABOUT THE CHESAPEAKE MERMAID

The Chesapeake Mermaid makes appearances at events throughout the region. She invites us to explore the Chesapeake watershed on a quest for innovative solutions to the natural world's toughest problems. She is a leader among volunteers and encourages the public to get involved in environmental programs. Become a part of her journey at chesapeakemermaid.com or summon her to an event by writing to info@chesapeakemermaid.com

Watch for other great adventures from The Chesapeake Mermaid

ChesapeakeMermaid.com

♩

*Boom Boom Boom Boom
Boom Boom Boom*

**A giant change,
Is coming soon,
It starts in you and me.
Our lasting mark,
Can be a scar,
When careless steps we take.**

*Boom Boom Boom Boom
Boom Boom Boom*

**Begin a wave,
And make it strong,
How wonderful to see.
My lasting mark,
will be for good,
With each new choice I make.**

*Boom Boom Boom Boom
Boom Boom Boom*

**My lasting mark,
will be for good,
With each new choice I make.**

CPSIA information can be obtained
at www.ICGtesting.com
Printed in the USA
BVHW050722200319
543151BV00001B/1/P